EASY START

The little brown dog

Series editor: Keith Gaines

Illustrated by Margaret de Souza

Nelson

"I want a pet,"
said Kim.
"I wanted a fish and
I wanted a frog.
Now I want a dog.

Please can I have a dog, Mum?
Rob's got a dog and
I want one."

"It will soon be your birthday,"
said Kim's Mum.
"You can have a dog
for your birthday."

"Oh good," said Kim.
"Can we go to the pet shop?"

Kim and her Mum went to the pet shop.

"Which dog shall we have?"
said Kim.
"There are lots of them."

A little brown dog
jumped up at Kim.

Then he fell down.

Then he looked up at Kim.

"I like this little brown dog,"
said Kim.
"Can we have this one?"

"Yes, I like him, too,"
said Kim's Mum.

They took the little brown dog
home.

"Can I play with him in the garden?"
said Kim.

"Yes," said her Mum,
"but don't forget to
stay with him."

But Kim did forget.

She went in to get a drink.

When she came out,
the little brown dog was not there.

They looked in the road.

The little brown dog was not there.

They looked in the house.

The little brown dog was not there.

"Go and get your coat,"
said Kim's Mum.
"We will go and look for him."